ART SMART

QEB Publishing

Editor: Lauren Taylor
Design: Tall Tree Ltd www.talltreebooks.co.uk
Illustrator: Tom Connell

Copyright © QEB Publishing 2012

First published in the United States in 2013 by
QEB Publishing, Inc
3 Wrigley, Suite A
Irvine, CA 92618

www.qed-publishing.co.uk

A catalogue record for this book is available from the Library of Congress.

ISBN 978 1 78171 334 1

Printed in China

Picture credits
(t=top, b=bottom, l=left, r=right, c=centre, fc=front cover, bc=back cover)
Mark Winwood: 8cr, 8bl, 9tr, 9c, 9bl, 21cl, 38cr, 38bl, 39tr, 39cl, 39br, 43br, 55br, 61br, 65br, 79br, 87b, 99br
Philip Wilkins: 6cl, 7tr, 7cl, 7br, 10cl, 10br, 11tr, 11cl, 11br, 12cr, 12br, 13tr, 13c, 13b 14tl, 14cr, 14bl, 15tl, 15b, 16cl, 17tl, 17bl, 18cr, 18bl, 19tr, 19cl, 19br, 20bl, 21tr, 21br, 22cr, 22bl, 23tl, 23cr, 23b, 24cr, 24bl, 25tl, 25cr, 25bl, 26cr, 26bl, 27tr, 27cl, 27br, 28tl, 28cr, 28bl, 29tr, 29cl, 29b, 32bl, 33tl, 33cr, 33bl, 34cl, 34c, 34br, 35tl, 35c, 36cl, 36br, 37tl, 37cr, 37b, 49br, 40cl, 41tr, 41cr, 41b, 42c, 42bl, 43tl, 43cr, 44c, 44bl, 45tl, 45c, 46cl, 46b, 47tr, 47c, 48c, 49tr, 49cl, 49cr, 49bl, 50cr, 50bl, 51tl, 51cl, 51b, 52cr, 52bl, 53tl, 53cr, 53b, 57br, 59br, 67br, 69br, 71br 73br, 75br, 77br, 81c, 83b, 85l, 89br, 91bl, 93b, 95bl, 97br, 101b
Shutterstock: 8cr, BonD80; 8tr, 8bl, 9br, 66br, 76br George Filyagin; 10tr, 12cl, 22tr, 28tr, 33tc, 38bl Alexandr Makarov, 10br, 19tr, 22tc, 24bl, 30br, 31cl, 32tl 34bl, 46tr, Evyatar Dayan; 10cr, 33tr, BonD80; 12tr, 16cr, 44cr, 46bl, 84tr, 90tr, shutswis; 14t, 15b, 16tr, 22tr, 22bl, 28tr Kitch Bain; 17cr, 33cr, 61bl, 76tr, 79tr magicoven; 18bl, 32cl, 32-33c, 69br, Nattika; 21tr, 24bc, 33tl, 62tr, 69tr artpoem; 24tr, 46cr Alex Moe, 24tc, 30tl, 37bl, 37tr, 50-51t, 71cl, 80, 82tr, 100br, Picsfive; 50-51c, 56br, 71c, 78l, Africa Studio; 30tc, 31cb, Olha Ukhal; 31tr, advent; 34tr, Olly; 36bl, 47tl, Gayvoronskaya_Yana; 38cr, Litvinenko Anastasia; 38br, NitroCephal; 42c, de2marco; 45tr, Jakub Ko≈°t√°l; 58br, discrupture; 60c oksana2010; 70, Kazyavka; 71tr, FrameAngel;78tr Anteromite; 78c, SeDmi; 84cl, 90br, 100tc pukach; 96tc, 99br, Garsya; 98br, Vasily Kovalev; 92, jcjgphotography

At the top of the page for each project you will find this handy key. It will tell you the difficulty level to expect from each project:

Quick Creative Fix

These projects are quick, easy, and perfect for a beginner.

Sharpen Your Skills

Confident with your beginner skills? Move onto these slightly tougher projects.

Ready For a Challenge

For a challenging project you can really get stuck into.

Creative Masterpiece

Think you can tackle the toughest creative projects? Have a go at these.

Note to Adults:
Some children might be able to do some or all of these projects on their own, while others might need more help. These are projects that you can work on together, not only to avoid any problems or accidents, but also to share in the fun of making art.

ART SMART

Traci Bunkers • Kath Durkin • Melanie Grimshaw • Wendy Walker

QEB Publishing

CONTENTS

DRAW IT!

PAINT IT!

PRINT IT!

FADING SHADING

Perfect your shading skills to create this layered pencil, moonlit landscape.

YOU WILL NEED:

- Selection of drawing pencils
- Letter-sized paper
- A penny

1 Practice shading with the side of a pencil point to make long strokes in the same direction. Try a soft pencil like a B or 2B, and don't press too hard. Add another layer over the first set, but going in a different direction.

2 Build up more layers of pencil in different directions and with strokes of different length until you feel confident shading from dark to light.

3 Draw out a 5 x 5 inch square. Draw some light, simple pencil lines from one side of the square to the other. Your lines might suggest sky, land, water, trees, or buildings. Draw around a penny to make the moon.

4 Begin your fading shading in the bottom shape. The fade can go upward or downward.

5 Make sure you shade each section in the same direction so that each one contrasts against the one next to it.

Sharpen your pencil regularly to keep your shading even.

FROTTAGE BUTTERFLIES

Build layers of textures and colors. Frottage comes from a French word, and means "rub."

YOU WILL NEED:

- Textured surfaces for rubbing
- Paper
- Colored pencils and crayons
- HB pencil
- Photograph of a butterfly

1 Choose a textured surface and place a sheet of paper over it. With a colored pencil or crayon, make a rubbing by coloring firmly over it with strokes in the same direction.

2 Experiment with all of your surfaces, using different colors and varying how firmly you make the rubbing.

8

3 Prepare a new sheet of paper with a background layer of one type of rubbing. Draw the outline of a butterfly with an HB pencil. You could trace a photograph of a butterfly, if you like.

4 Add another layer of a different texture in a different color inside the wing shapes.

5 Have fun inventing the patterns and strong colors of your butterfly. Fill in all the shapes, using colored pencils for the finer detail.

Netting, feathers, leaves, burlap, wood grain, wallpaper...you can make rubbings with so many things!

JUNGLE LINES

Create a jungle full of exotic animals and plants. All you need is pencils and pens.

YOU WILL NEED:

- Paper
- Black fineliner pens in various thicknesses
- HB pencil

1 Practice drawing some lines with your markers. Experiment with creating textures and patterns. What type of lines make things appear closer or farther away?

2 With a pencil, lightly draw the outlines of leaf and plant shapes. These are planning lines that you will not see on your final drawing.

3 Add and overlap more jungle shapes at the bottom of the picture. This will form the foreground of your scene. Add tree trunks to the background too.

4 Look at the spaces you have left and imagine where you can place animals, hiding or peering out from behind the jungle plants. Keep adding more plants or flowers until it becomes a dense and exotic rain forest.

5 Redraw your planning lines using black fineliner pens. Look at your experiments from step 1 to help you decide which kinds of lines work best to describe the different areas of your jungle.

COOL CATS

Capture these cool, colorful characters for fun stickers.

1 Using the heavy drawing paper, draw and cut out a template of a cat's head to use over and over again.

2 Using sheets of different colored sticker paper, draw around your template and cut out the cat's head shapes.

3 On a separate sheet of paper, practice drawing different faces and expressions.

4 Choose the faces you like best and draw them onto your cutout heads.

5 You can stick your cool cats wherever you like! The repeat design would also make a brilliant wrapping paper.

Using a simple template is a quick way to make repeat patterns.

BLAST OFF!

Use simple perspective drawing to launch a rocket into space!

YOU WILL NEED:

- Paper
- HB pencil
- Ruler
- Eraser
- Colored markers

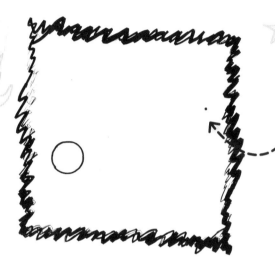

1 Begin by drawing a dot and a circle, some distance apart, using a pencil. You will need to erase them later.

2 Using a ruler, draw planning lines against the top and bottom curve of the circle to the dot. You will see a tube shape forming.

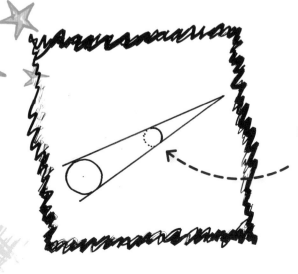

3 Draw another circle for a curved end to the tube shape, halfway down your planning lines.

4 Turn the tube into a rocket by adding a triangular tip and some wings. Erase the planning lines and strengthen the lines you want to keep with darker pencil or pen. The dot becomes a planet millions of light years away.

5 Use your imagination. Add detail to build up your scene in color.

Sweeping lines and curves will add speed and movement to your drawing.

MAIL IT!

Send your postcard creations across the world or simply mail them to yourself.

YOU WILL NEED:

- Postcard, used or new
- Collage materials, such as patterned paper, old stamps, pictures, and stickers
- Scissors
- Glue
- Colored markers
- Postage stamp

1 Decide on the type of postcard you want. It could be old and written on, or blank so you can start from scratch.

2 Think about how you want to decorate your postcard. You could decide to say "Hello" in lots of different languages.

hola

hi

hello

salut

konnichawa

hello

bonjour

ciao

3 You could use old envelopes with patterns, stamps, postmarks, and torn edges to make a collage. Overlap your collage pieces to make a patchwork and think about how you want to fill in the spaces.

4 Arrange your collage before gluing it all into place on your postcard. You can use markers or stickers to add more color and interest.

Start a collection of scraps of any items that you find interesting to use for collage creations.

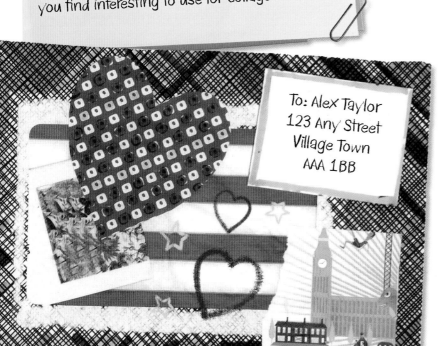

To: Alex Taylor
123 Any Street
Village Town
AAA 1BB

5 Make another collage for the other side of your postcard, and don't forget to leave space for the address. Now all you need to do is mail it to the lucky recipient!

LEOPARD SPOT PHOTO FRAME

YOU WILL NEED:

- Ruler
- HB pencil
- White cardstock or heavy drawing paper
- Watercolor pencils
- A bowl of water
- Scissors
- Glue
- A photograph
- An empty CD case

Animal prints can make really great patterns and are easier to draw than you might think!

1 Draw a 5 x 5 inch (12 x 12 cm) square on your paper or card. Choose the colors for your fur base. Yellows, oranges, reddish browns, and dark browns will work well. Working with the lightest color first, begin to overlap your colors loosely, with long, fast strokes, to suggest a furry texture. Fill the whole square with your colors.

2 Practice drawing leopard spots. No two spots are exactly the same. They almost look like wiggly "O" and "C" letter shapes.

3 Carefully copy the spots onto your colored square and fill them in with a dark color.

4 Dip your finger into a bowl of water and use it to print furry "splatter" effects on your spots. When it is completely dry, use the colored pencils to add a final layer of squiggly, furry texture.

5 Cut out your colored square and stick your photograph in the center with a few drops of glue. Slide your picture carefully into the front of the CD case. It should fit perfectly and the frame will stand up on its own when it is left open.

What other types of animal print could you make?

MUSICAL DOODLES

Doodling to music stops you thinking too hard and allows your imagination to break free.

YOU WILL NEED:

- Your fingers, to make prints
- An ink pad, made from a sponge soaked with a few drops of ink and placed on a bowl
- Your favorite music
- A variety of paper
- Markers and fineliner pens

1 Put on your music and take a moment to clear your mind. When you feel ready, press your fingers onto the ink pad and make fingerprint rhythms that dance across the page. Do the rhythms you make change if you change the style of music?

2 Choose your favorite fingerprint rhythms and stare at the shapes. What do you see? Use regular or fineliner pens to doodle the different characters you see. Maybe you see animals.

3 Add as much details as you like to your doodles, using a pencil first if you need more confidence.

4 Try varying the thickness of the lines you make to add more impact. Would dancing people be drawn with bolder lines than fluttering birds?

5 You could also try doodling on different types of paper. There's no limit to the different creations you can make when you free your imagination!

What you see in your fingerprint rhythms will be individual to you.

SPIRAL ART

What creative pictures can you make using only spirals?

1 Practice drawing spirals using a pencil. They can be loose or tightly curled.

2 Add a simple head and tail, and you have a snail with a spiral shell. Color your snail with markers, giving the spiral a shell pattern

3 Use your imagination and find out what other pictures you can make using spirals. Always start with a simple spiral and see where you go from there.

4 Once you have found your favorite spiral drawings, you can build up a scene of spirals. Here, spiral snails are crawling among spiral trees and plants. Color your drawing to bring your scene to life.

Coloring spirals with patterns will make each one look different.

UP AND DOWN FACES

Facial expressions are always changing. **Our** faces can light **up** with joy or hang **down** with sadness.

1 Begin with an oval shape for a head. Find the middle of the oval and add two lines to make a cross. This shows where your features will be drawn.

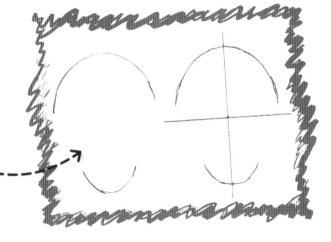

2 To draw a happy face, mark lines for the eyes that go upward at the corners on the eye line and a mouth that curves upward. Add the eyebrows, eye shapes, and lips.

YOU WILL NEED:

- HB pencil
- Paper
- Black fineliner pen
- Eraser

3 Adding cheekbones and dimples will make the smile even stronger. Ears, nose, and hair will complete the face.

4 Now make another face in the same way, but make the lines of the eyes and mouth go down at the corners.

5 Use a fineliner pen to strengthen your drawn lines and then erase the unwanted planning lines.

Making the angles more extreme will make an extremely happy or sad face!

SAY IT WITH FLOWERS

Create flowers with glitter glue and pastels for a special gift card.

YOU WILL NEED:

- Real flowers or pictures of flowers to study
- HB pencil
- 4 x 4 in. (10 x 10 cm) square of heavy paper
- White glue or glitter glue in an easy squeeze bottle
- Colored soft pastels
- Cotton balls
- Letter-sized cardstock
- Hair spray or artist's adhesive

1 Before you begin your design, practice simple flower structures, by studying real flowers. Choose the flower shape you like best and draw its outline lightly with pencil to fit snugly onto your paper or card. Keep the shapes in your drawing really simple.

2 Draw over the pencil lines with the glitter glue. Touch the tip of the glue bottle directly onto the paper. Give a little squeeze and let the glue flow in an even line. Pulling the glue bottle toward you is always better than pushing it away from you. Let the glue dry completely.

3 Choose two different colored pastels that will blend well together. One should be a dark color and the other lighter. Working from the center of the flower, add a little of the dark color inside each of the petal shapes, then add the lighter color to half fill each of the petals. Overlap the colors slightly.

4 Carefully blend your colors with a clean finger or a cotton ball, ensuring that the color stays inside the shapes and fades gradually out to the ends of the petals. You can add extra details with the edge of a pastel. Fix your drawing with hair spray or artist's adhesive so that it doesn't smudge.

5 To make your drawing into a gift card, you will need to fold your letter-sized cardstock in half and carefully glue your drawing onto the front.

Draw a stem with multiple flowers on it, and color them in the same way.

MICROSCOPIC ART

The world looks very different at a microscopic level. If you had microscopic eyes, what treasures would you find?

1 Begin with a single dot which will begin your "microbe." Make your microbe grow "legs" with lines. Keep it simple to begin with by only using four legs. Then add more dots to the ends.

2 Expand your microbe from these new dots.

3 Keep adding and growing more legs from each dot. Make your microbe as big as you like.

28

4 Go back to the middle dot and begin to invent the body of your microbe.

5 Use your imagination to let it grow and grow, then add color to bring life to your drawings.

Fill your paper with microscopic designs. What will your dots and lines become?

PICASSO SELF PORTRAIT

YOU WILL NEED:

- Tracing paper
- HB pencil
- Photographs of yourself or a mirror
- Heavy drawing paper
- Acrylic paint
- Paint palette
- Paintbrush

Picasso created weird and wonderful portraits. Here's how to make your own!

1 On tracing paper, draw a straight face portrait of yourself in pencil. Trace over a photograph of yourself or use a mirror.

2 On another piece of tracing paper, draw another portrait of yourself of the same size—this time from a profile view.

3 Draw a third portrait of yourself on another sheet of tracing paper of the same size—this time from a three-quarter view.

4 Take all three of your portraits and layer them on top of each other. Through the tracing paper, you should be able to see all three drawings. Line them up so your head is in the same place in each one.

5 On a piece of drawing paper, transfer your portraits (see page 113), picking out the different features to make a "jumbled" portrait. Thicken the lines you want to stand out.

Use acrylic paint to color your portrait. The colors can be as strange as the portrait itself!

COLOR WHEEL RUBBING

Explore the colors in a color wheel with this rainbow design.

1 Collect some leaves from your garden or local park. Make sure they are different sizes and have some interesting patterns and textures.

2 Place your leaves under a sheet of thin paper, and practice making rubbings of them in different colors, using colored pencils.

3 Next, arrange six similar-sized leaves in a fanned circle. Lay a clean sheet of paper on top and rub over the leaves in the colors of the color wheel. These colors are: red, orange, yellow, green, blue, and purple.

4 Using the watercolor paint and a paintbrush, practice blending out the six colors, so they go from bold to faint. Use more paint to make the colors dark and more water to make them lighter.

5 Finish your color wheel by applying this painting technique around your leaf circle. Blend the different colors together when they meet to make new shades and tones.

Use this picture for color reference when painting other projects.

EASTER CHICK GIFTCARD

Combine painting and collage to make a bold design for a giftcard.

1 On a piece of cardboard, draw an Easter chick design using simple shapes. Make sure your design will fit on an letter-sized paper.

Yellow acrylic, with gold metallic paint dabbed over the surface using a piece of cardstock

Orange and yellow acrylic mixed together to make a bold orange

A dark violet for adding strong details

2 On a separate piece of cardstock, experiment with different colors of paint to decide how to color your chick design.

Violet and white acrylic to make a pale purple

34

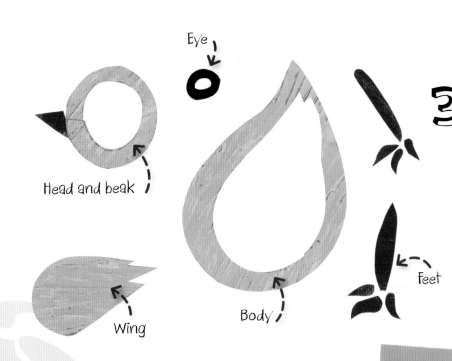

Eye

Head and beak

Wing

Body

Feet

3 Choose your favorite paint colors to paint the shapes of your chick. Once the paint is dry, cut these pieces out with scissors.

4 Assemble your pieces on your folded letter-sized cardstock. You can also add a background and a border for decoration. Glue all the pieces into place.

You can make painted collage giftcards for any occassion! How about this scary pumpkin design?

DOODLE PAINTINGS

Doodling can free your imagination. You can get even more creative by painting the shapes you make.

YOU WILL NEED:

- Heavy drawing paper
- Waterproof fineliner pen
- Watercolor paint
- Paintbrush
- Paint palette

1 Take your piece of paper and the fineliner pen, and doodle a random line all around your paper. The line can circle, curl, or zigzag—anything you want!

2 When you've finished, look for pictures you could make from the shapes. If you look closely, this doodle could look like a duck and a mushroom.

3 Using your pen, fill in some extra details on the pictures you see in your doodle.

4 When you feel confident enough, paint your doodle picture to really bring it to life! You can experiment with your paint on a separate piece of paper first.

Every doodle you draw will make a new and exciting picture!

CREATE A MONSTER

Get imaginative with this monster character! Coloring with wax and paint can make great patterns.

1 To sketch out your monster character, draw egg shapes to make up the body, legs, arms, and head.

2 Link them together and add details, such as fingers, toes, horns, and facial features. You could even make him hairy!

3 Before you add color to your monster, experiment on a separate piece of paper. Take a candle and draw patterns and textures that you'd like to use on your monster. Then paint over them with watercolor paint. The patterns you drew should come through.

4 Draw the wax patterns on your monster. Think about what patterns you want him to have on different parts of his body. Paint your monster with watercolor paint.

5 Finally, use a black fineliner pen to add definition and detail to your monster. You can even add a background in a similar style!

Turn the page to the next project to give your monster a friend!

MONSTER PETS

In the last project you created your own monster. Now keep him company with a cool monster pet!

1 Begin by drawing egg shapes to make different characters. Use your imagination—they can look like whatever you want them to!

2 Work up these shapes, adding fur, scales, toes, eyes, and antennae— anything you want!

3 Before you add color to your monster pets, take a clean sheet of paper and experiment with different effects. Try painting with other things besides a paintbrush. These could be things like fabric, your fingers, or a sponge. Apply a small amount of paint to them and press or dab them onto the paper.

fabric textures

fingerprints

aluminum

sponge

4 Choose your favorite painting techniques and use them to color your monster pets. Think about what textures your different pets would have, depending on what features they have.

5 Finally, use a black fineliner pen to add definition and detail to your monster pets.

There's no limit to what your monster creations can look like!

GLOWING FISH

Using this unique painting technique, this colorful fish appears to almost glow.

1 First practice drawing fish shapes. Use rounded diamond shapes for the bodies and triangle shapes for the tails. Practice adding details, such as eyes, mouth, fins, and scales.

2 Draw your final big fish on your thick paper, then color in the fish and background using oil pastels and pressing very hard. Make it as colorful as possible and cover the entire paper. On a separate piece of paper, color in a solid, smaller rectangle. This will be your test piece.

3 Take your black oil pastel and paint over your oil pastel fish design. Cover the entire page, but leave a fine outline, so you can see where your fish drawing is. Paint over your test piece too.

4 On your test piece, use your sharp object to scratch away at the black to reveal the colors underneath. Experiment scratching out different patterns, using different tools to get different effects. Here are some suggested pattern ideas. Be very careful with anything you use that is sharp.

5 Now scratch into your fish picture. If you feel confident enough, you can add more fish to make a full ocean scene.

Be careful not to scratch so hard that you go through the paper!

STENCIL SNOWFLAKES

Stencils are a fun and an easy way to make lots of different patterns with paint.

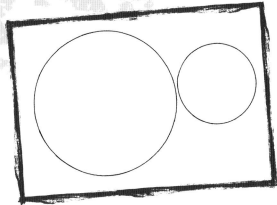

1 Using the cups, draw two circles on a piece of paper. Cut the circles out, fold them in half, then fold them in half again.

2 On each of the folded circles, draw a different design. Cut out the shapes and unfold your circles.

3 Using sticky tack, stick your stencils to your cartridge paper. Lightly dip a cotton ball into the paint and dab all over the stencils. Peel the stencils off and wait for the paint to dry before adding more.

4 Ask an adult to help you with the spray paint. You must make sure you are in a large room with an open window or outside. Layer the stencils however you like. Stick your pencils to the paper, as before, and spray a light coat of paint over the top.

5 Layer your stencils any way you want. You can even stick them onto your painting afterwards for a collage effect.

There are so many different shapes you can make with circle stencils.

45

PERSONALIZED BOOKMARK

Use the initials of your name to make a creative design for a bookmark.

1 On your card, draw two horizontal lines 2 inches (5 cm) apart. Write your initials between these lines. Use a ruler to help you.

2 Using your ruler again, make the letters thick and chunky.

3 Using scissors, cut these letters out. You will use them as stencils for your bookmark.

4 From your other sheet of card, cut out a strip 2.5 in. (5.5 cm) wide and 9 in. (23 cm) long. Use your stencils to create an interesting pattern on your bookmark. You can even flip them around and use them back to front.

5 Using watercolor paint, paint your bookmark using bright, complementary colors. Either yellow and purple, red and green, or blue and orange. Cut it out with scissors.

By arranging your initials in different ways, you can make bookmarks that have different shapes and patterns.

AMAZING MOSAIC

Create your own colored and textured mosaics to make a cool mosaic design.

Paint mixed with sand

Thin paint applied with large brush

Dried paint with white glue patterns applied on top

1 On the cardstock paper, create different-colored or textured backgrounds. You can add sand or glitter to give the paint texture, or use your fingers or a sponge to make patterns. Let them dry completely.

Paint mixed with glitter

Paint dabbed onto paper with a small sponge

Paint swirled into patterns with fingertips

2 Using scissors, cut up your colored backgrounds into pieces. Try to cut them into shapes that will fit together easily, such as squares, rectangles, and trianges. Make sure the largest pieces are no more than 2 x 2 in. (4 x 4 cm).

3 On a large sheet of drawing paper, draw a 12 x 12 in. (24 x 24 cm) grid, and divide it up by 2 x 2 in. (4 x 4 cm) squares.

4 Now get creative! Make a mosaic pattern on your grid by gluing the shapes onto the grid.

The patterns and color combinations you can make are endless!

FRAMED SUNSET

The artist Howard Hodgkin uses large brushes and sweeping brushstrokes to make paintings that look like sunsets.

1 Ask an adult to remove the glass from the picture frame, so you are left with the frame and backing only.

2 Look at your sunset pictures and decide on the background colors to paint your frame. Use large, horizontal brushstrokes to paint sweeping color across the frame.

3 Once dry, choose other colors from your sunset pictures to layer over the background. Add these colors using the same sweeping brushstrokes.

4 Keep on layering colors until you are happy with your sunset. Remember to keep the brushstrokes loose and flowing.

5 Wait until your frame is completely dry before hanging on the wall!

Search on the Internet for "Howard Hodgkin" to see beautiful sunset paintings just like yours!

PATCHWORK LANDSCAPE

Countryside landscapes can look a lot like a patchwork quilt. This inspired artist David Hockney to make really colorful paintings.

1 Look at your countryside picture and plan out your patchwork fields using light pencil lines. Stick lengths of masking tape around the edges of the paper. This will keep your painting neat.

Foreground

Middle

Background

2 Notice the colors in your countryside picture. What shades would be best to use for the foreground, middle and background? Do the colors get lighter as they move into the distance? Experiment with the colors you would like to use.

Grass: long, thin brush, dabbed onto paper on its side

Hedges: painting with a cotton ball

Cornfields: bold red and yellow stripes

3 On a separate sheet of paper, experiment with the brushstrokes you can make to suggest different parts of the landscape.

4 Paint your landscape, one patchwork square at a time. Use your experiments to decide what colors and techniques to apply to each area.

5 Finally, once your painting is dry, peel off the masking tape.

You could even paint the scene outside your window.

PRINTED PET T-SHIRT

You can liven up plain T-shirts with this easy printing method.

YOU WILL NEED:

- Cardboard or folded newspaper
- T-shirt, washed
- Fabric paint, in various colors
- Flat paint palette
- Sponge brush
- Small paintbrush

1 Insert a piece of cardboard or folded newspapers inside the T-shirt. This will stop the paint soaking through to the back. Make sure the shirt is smooth and not wrinkled.

2 Squeeze some paint onto your paint palette, then use a sponge brush to spread it into a thin layer. Use several colors for a more vibrant design.

3 Draw a picture of your pet, or a favorite animal, into the paint with a paintbrush. Everything will print backward, so if you include any writing, be sure to write it backward.

4 Carefully place the painted side of the paint palette on the T-shirt where you want the design to print. Press down on the palette to be sure the whole picture will print.

5 Carefully peel the palette off the T-shirt and let the paint dry. Heat set the design according to the directions on the fabric paint.

Practice your design on paper first to get the best outcome!

PICTURE PERFECT

Decorate a picture frame with stamps you can make and change yourself!

YOU WILL NEED:

- Poster paint, in various colors
- Plastic cup
- Unvarnished wooden picture frame, with backing and glass removed
- Paintbrush or sponge brush
- Modeling clay
- Sharp pencil and items to make texture
- Thin sponge

1 Pour a small amount of light colored paint into the plastic cup. Paint the front and sides of the frame with the paint. Let it dry.

2 Roll a small piece of modeling clay into a short log shape. Pinch one end to make a small handle and flatten the other end for the stamp.

3 Use a pencil to draw a design into the flat part of the stamp. You could also make a texture by pressing different items into the clay, such as a straw or the pattern on the sole of a shoe.

4 Squeeze a small amount of paint onto the sponge. Use your fingers to spread it around. Press the stamp onto the paint on the sponge, then stamp onto the frame. Repeat to create whatever pattern you like.

5 When the frame is dry, you can stamp the frame again using a different color or design.

This would make a unique gift!

COOL KID SHOES

Impress everyone with these arty shoes that you painted yourself.

1 Stuff the shoes with scrunched-up newspaper so that they hold their shape. Apply the masking tape to make a stripy pattern on the shoes.

2 Squeeze a small amount of paint onto a paper plate. Dip the paintbrush into the paint, then tap the brush between the masking tape stripes to color in the spaces.

58

3 When the paint is dry, remove the masking tape.

4 Place the stickers onto the unpainted areas of the shoes. Using a different paint color, tap the paintbrush around the edges of the stickers, coloring in the stripes.

5 When the paint is dry, remove the stickers. Add some decoration with fabric pens or color in the white shapes, if you like.

Add some funky laces to make your shoes even more colorful.

ARTIST'S SELF-PORTRAIT

Every artist should make a self-portrait, and printing gives you a unique way to do it!

1 Cut your cardboard a little smaller than your piece of paper. Draw your self-portrait onto the cardboard using a marker pen.

2 Trace over the lines of your self-portrait drawing with white glue, then press the thick yarn or string into the glue. Let the glue dry.

60

3 Pour a small amount of paint into the plastic cup. Dip your sponge brush into the paint, then brush it onto the glued yarn.

4 Before the paint dries, place your paper on top of the self-portrait. With your hands, push down on the paper, carefully moving your hands around so that the paint prints onto the paper.

5 Lift the paper off the printing cardboard and let the paint dry. Decorate your printed portrait with things like crayons, marker pens, and glitter glue.

You can use this method to create a picture of anything you like!

WICKED WRAPPING PAPER

Printing is great for creating repeating patterns—perfect for making your own wrapping paper!

YOU WILL NEED:

- Marker pen
- Adhesive craft foam
- Scissors
- Empty cardboard juice can
- Masking tape
- Poster paint, in various colors
- Paint palette
- Sponge brush
- A large sheet of paper

1 Draw some simple shapes, such as stars, hearts, and zigzags, on the craft foam. Cut the shapes out with scissors.

2 Ask an adult to tape the lid back onto the can with masking tape. This will help it hold its shape.

3 Stick the foam shapes onto the can, leaving an inch free at each end for rolling with your hands.

4 Squeeze some paint onto your paint palette. Apply the paint onto the foam shapes with the sponge brush.

5 Roll the can over the paper, printing the foam shapes pattern. Apply more paint when you need to. When the paint is dry, use a different color to print on top of the first layer.

You can make so many different designs with this method!

TERRIFIC TREASURE BOX

Transform a simple box into a colorful treasure box to store all your odds and ends.

YOU WILL NEED:

- Cardboard box with lid
- Poster paint, in various colors
- Small dish of water
- Paint palette
- Paintbrush
- Pencil
- Pop-up sponges (alternatively, use any thin sponge)
- Scissors
- Crayons, marker pens and glitter glue (optional)

1 Paint the box and lid one color.

2 Draw some simple shapes onto the pop-up sponges with a pencil, then cut them out with scissors.

3 Place the sponge shapes in water to let them expand. Then squeeze the water out of them. You won't need to do this if you're using normal sponge or foam.

4 Pour a small amount of paint onto your palette. Dip the sponge stamps into the paint so that the bottom surface is covered, then stamp it onto the box or lid. Stamp your box with different colors and stamps to make the pattern you want.

5 When the paint is dry, you can decorate your box with crayons, marker pens, glitter glue, or anything else you'd like.

BRILLIANT BIRTHDAY CARDS

YOU WILL NEED:

- Construction paper for card and for stencil
- Scissors
- Tape
- Acrylic paint
- Plastic cup
- Fat paintbrush
- Crayons, stickers, marker pens, and glitter glue

When you make your own birthday cards, you can personalize them for the lucky recipient.

1 For the stencil, draw a small, simple outline of a picture on the paper that you can cut out.

2 Cut a straight line to the picture from the edge of the card, then carefully cut the shape out, ending back at the straight line. Tape the paper back together along the cut line, completely covering the cut.

3 Fold the paper for the card in half, then open out flat. Place the stencil on the right half of the card.

4 Pour a small amount of paint into the plastic cup. Dip the paintbrush into the paint. While holding the stencil down with one hand, tap the brush around the inside and edges of the cutout area. Do this until the whole shape is filled in with paint.

5 Lift the paper stencil off and let the paint dry. Repeat with different colors until you are happy with the design. When the paint is dry, personalize the card with crayons, stickers, marker pens, and glitter glue.

The shape cutout of the stencil can be used as a mask. Use it like a stencil, tapping the paint around the edges of the shape.

PRINTED GIFT STICKERS

Customize your own gift stickers using floral foam.

YOU WILL NEED:

- Sharp pencil
- Small rectangle of dry floral foam (oasis)
- Poster paint
- Thin sponge, same size as the floral foam
- Paper, for testing
- Towel, folded in half
- Label or sticker paper
- Marker pens
- Scissors

1 Draw a simple design onto one side of the floral foam, piercing the surface of the foam with the pencil as you draw. Carve out a rectangular space at the bottom, leaving a border. This will leave a space to write in.

2 Squeeze a small amount of paint onto a sponge, then use your fingers to spread it around the surface. Place a piece of testing paper on top of a folded towel.

3 Press the carved side of the floral foam onto the paint on the sponge, then stamp it onto the test paper. If the design is faint in areas, redraw it into the foam, piercing deeper. Test the stamp again. You might need to do this a few times to get a print you are happy with.

68

4 Place the label paper on top of the towel. Press the foam onto the paint sponge and stamp onto the label paper. Repeat this until the label paper is covered. Add more paint to the sponge when needed.

5 Use marker pens to color in the white areas of the stamps. Finally, cut the sheet into individual gift stickers.

Jack   Olivia   Ruby   Thomas

Perfect for Christmas if you need to tag a lot of presents!

VEGGIE-PRINT BAG

Design your own bag using printing objects from around your home.

1 Lay the bag flat and put a piece of cardboard or folded newspaper inside it. This will stop the paint from soaking through to the other side. Make sure the bag is smooth and not wrinkled.

2 Ask an adult to cut some fruits or vegetables in half or into small pieces. Remove any seeds.

3 Squeeze a small amount of paint into a plastic cup. Dip the sponge brush into the paint, then brush it onto the cut side of a piece of fruit or vegetable.

4 Press the fruit or vegetable stamp onto the bag. Continue printing with different pieces and colors, making a picture or design. Let it dry, then print the other side of the bag.

5 With a sponge brush, brush paint onto the wheels of a toy car. Roll the wheels along the fabric to make printed tire tracks. You can use almost any object or toy you like to print with, but remember to ask for permission first!

Don't eat any of the fruits or vegetables that you have painted!

PERSONALIZED STATIONERY

Print your own stationery for letters, thank you notes, or invitations!

YOU WILL NEED:

- Blank stationery paper and envelopes
- Small toys or household objects for stenciling
- Acrylic paint, in various colors
- Plastic cups
- Fat paintbrush
- Sponge brush

1 Open the stationery paper and place it flat, with the outside facing up, in the direction you want the card to be. Place the object to be used as a stencil on the half of the card that is the front. Here, a flat plastic animal has been used.

2 Squeeze a small amount of paint into a plastic cup. Dip the paintbrush into the paint. While holding the object on the paper with one hand, tap the brush around the edges of the object and any cut-out areas. Do this until the whole shape is stenciled with paint.

3 After the paint is dry, stencil again on a different area with the same object, or a different one. Use a different color of paint if you like. You can also stencil the half of the card that is the back.

4 You can also try printing the objects instead of stenciling. With a sponge brush, apply paint onto the object. Stamp the object onto the paper, pressing down all of the edges. Repeat as many times as you like.

5 Stencil and stamp the envelope to match.

Be creative—there are loads of colors and designs to choose from.

BUBBLE WAND BOARD

Liven up a plain bulletin board with colorful stenciling.

YOU WILL NEED:

- Acrylic paint, in various colors
- Plastic cups
- Paintbrush or sponge brush
- Cork bulletin board
- Large bubble wand with shapes
- Fat paintbrush
- Paper towel
- Old toothbrush
- Felt-tip pens

1 Squeeze a small amount of paint into a plastic cup. Add a little water to thin the paint and stir. Paint the front and frame of the bulletin board. Let it dry.

2 Squeeze a small amount of a different colored paint into a cup. Place a bubble wand where you want it on the bulletin board. Dip the fat paintbrush into the paint. Hold the bubble wand flat with one hand and tap the brush in all the cut out spaces of the bubble wand.

3 Clean the bubble wand with a damp paper towel. Repeat the previous step, using a different color paint if you like, this time with the wand in another place. Continue stenciling with the same wand, or another one, until you have a design you're happy with. Remember to let the paint dry before stenciling on top of another design.

4 After the paint is dry, you can add to the design with felt-tip pens.

5 To finish, create a splatter pattern. Squeeze a small amount of paint onto an old toothbrush. With the bristles facing down, run your finger across the bristles toward you to splatter paint on the bulletin board.

Use colors to match the colors of your bedroom.

SUPER SKETCHBOOK

Every artist needs a sketchbook. Here's how to make your own!

YOU WILL NEED:

- Scissors
- Cardboard
- Heavy paper for the cover
- White glue in a squeeze bottle
- Crayons
- Paper for inside the book, about 5-8 sheets
- Hole punch
- Ribbon or yarn, three times the length of the book
- Marker pens and glitter glue

1 Cut the cardboard a little smaller than the paper for the cover. Draw any design you like onto the cardboard.

2 Trace over the lines of your picture with white glue and let it dry. The glue should dry in raised, hard lines. This is your rubbing plate.

3 Put the cover paper on top of the rubbing plate. Scribble over it with crayons to make the design appear, filling the whole paper.

4 Stack the cover and the inside paper together, and fold them in half. Open them back up. Punch a hole about 1 inch from each end on the fold. You will need to punch several sheets at a time instead of all of them together.

5 Stack the cover and pages together again. String the yarn or ribbon through the holes. Tie snugly on the outside to hold the book together. Decorate your sketchbook with marker pens and glitter glue.

Use lined paper for the inside pages and you can use this book as a journal!

LOVE-HEART GIFT BOX

Is a special occasion coming up? This cute gift box will be a great way to present your gift!

- Scissors
- Felt in assorted colors
- Pins
- Needle
- Embroidery thread
- Toy stuffing
- Ribbon
- Cardboard box with lid
- Fabric glue
- Buttons and any decorations you like, such as feathers or sequins.

1 For the heart, cut out two equal-sized pieces of felt. Pin these two pieces together.

2 Using a needle and thread, stitch the heart pieces together using a blanket stitch. Leave a small space to insert your toy stuffing, then stitch it completely closed when you have stuffed the heart.

3 Wrap a length of ribbon around the outside of your box, and secure it with fabric glue. You could also stitch on one or two separate felt heart shapes to the ribbon.

4 Gather a length of ribbon together in loops to create a flower shape. Stitch a button in the center to hold the ribbon in place.

5 Finally, glue the stuffed felt heart and ribbon flower to the box lid using fabric glue.

Make an Easter-themed box using colorful feathers for a cute Easter chick!

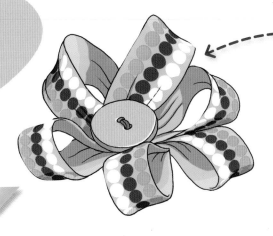

WOVEN MOBILE

This mobile will add a splash of color to your bedroom, and it's lots of fun to make!

1 With the end of a small ball of yarn, tie a knot around the center of two dowel rods. Secure the rods into a cross shape.

2 Weave the yarn over and around one dowel rod, then over and around the next, and so on with each rod. Make sure to keep the wool taut and keep your rods in the cross position.

3 Keep weaving and tie on new colors of yarn to make a striped effect. Stop when you have an inch or two of space left at both ends of each rod. Tie the loose end of the yarn in a knot to secure it.

4 Make a variety of different sized woven crosses and tie them together with yarn to make a hanging mobile. Finally, thread colorful beads onto any loose ends of yarn for decoration.

You can use different colors to match the colors of your bedroom!

SPACE PILLOWCASE

Want to create a theme for your bedroom? Printing on fabric can liven up plain pillowcases.

1 Cut a piece of cardboard to fit inside your pillowcase. Insert the cardboard into the pillowcase and lie it flat.

2 Squeeze different fabric paint colors onto separate paper plates.

3 Use objects, such as sponges, cotton spools and cardboard shapes, to print with. Dip them into the paint and press them onto the fabric. You can cut out rocket ship or star shapes from sponge and cardboard.

4 Print your pattern all over the front of the pillowcase. Once dry, turn over and repeat on the back.

5 Once completely dry, ask an adult to place a thin cloth over the pillowcase and slowly iron over it on a cool setting. This will seal the paint and stop it from cracking or washing off.

Get creative and use any colors and printing objects you like. How about a nature pattern?

POCKET ORGANIZER

keep your bedroom tidy and stylish at the same time with this fun organizer.

YOU WILL NEED:

- Scissors
- An old piece of clothing that has pockets
- Felt in assorted colors
- Pins
- Needle
- Embroidery thread
- Fabric glue
- Sequins and goggly eyes
- Long length of ribbon
- Wooden dowel rod

1 Cut a large rectangle from an old piece of clothing, including the pockets.

2 Cut out decorative felt shapes and pin these in place on the fabric. Stick on goggly eyes if you have made any animal shapes.

leaves

animal shapes

eyes

3 Stitch on the shapes using a running stitch. You can also glue or stitch on sequins to decorate your shapes.

4 Using a running stitch, sew a length of ribbon around the edge of the organizer to hide the rough edges and create a border.

5 Stitch two loops of ribbon to the top of the organizer and slip a wooden dowel rod through the loops so it can be hung.

Create felt shapes that show your favorite theme. The more colorful, the better!

HAIR TIE BIRD

You can create this cute, colorful bird for a show stopping hair accessory.

1 Cut out two equal-sized pieces of felt for the main body shape of your bird. Pin these two pieces together.

body pieces

2 Using a needle and thread, stitch around the outside of the body in either a blanket or running stitch, leaving a space of about 1/2 inch open.

3 Through this space, fill the body with toy stuffing, then stitch up the hole.

4 Cut out felt ovals for the face, a folded diamond for the beak and triangles for the feathers and ears. Glue or stitch these onto the body.

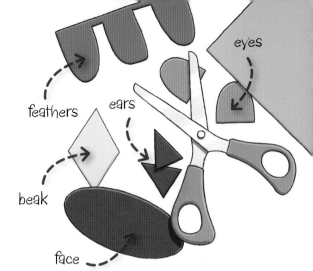

feathers

ears

eyes

beak

face

5 Attach feathers for wings and a pair of goggly eyes to make your bird come to life! Finally, stitch a hair tie to the back of the bird's body.

Make a pencil tie, using different felt shapes and colors to create any animal you want!

GET WELL CARD

This cute, colorful card will really brighten someone's day.

1 Lay three of the felt squares side by side and sew them together one by one, using a running stitch. Do this by holding two squares together and stitching along the very edge of one side. Repeat with the third square.

2 Repeat with the other squares to make three rows. Sew the rows together in the same way. Flip the quilt over so the stitching is on the back. Add a running stitch around the edge for decoration.

3 Make a small pillowcase by cutting out a rectangle of white felt and decorating around the edge in a running stitch.

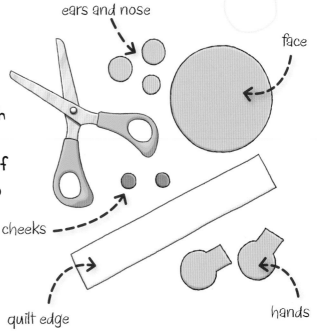

ears and nose

face

cheeks

quilt edge

hands

4 Cut out felt shapes for the face and hands. Stitch eyes and a mouth onto the face circle and glue this onto the pillowcase. Cut a strip of white felt to make a quilt edge to position the hands onto.

5 Using an embroidery needle, sew yarn around the head to make hair. Glue all the felt pieces onto a rectangle of backing felt and glue onto a folded piece of letter-sized cardstock

Who wouldn't feel better after receiving a beautiful card like this?

DINO DOORSTOP

This colorful fabric dinosaur will make the perfect little guard for your bedroom door.

1 With tailors' chalk, draw four equal-sided triangles on the patterned fabrics and felt. Make sure each side of each triangle is 6 inches (15 cm) long. Cut out the triangles.

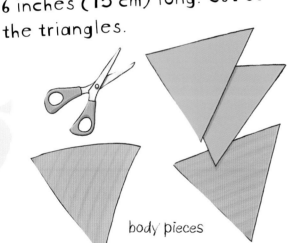

body pieces

2 With the patterned sides facing inward, use a running stitch to sew the triangles together at the sides to make a pyramid shape. Leave the final side open and turn the pyramid inside out.

90

3 Through the open side, fill the pyramid with dried beans. (You can use a paper cone to do this.) Sew up the open side with a blanket stitch.

tail

claws

4 Make a stuffed felt snout, two hands and a tail using felt shapes sewn together with a running stitch and stuffed with toy stuffing. Stitch these pieces onto the pyramid body.

5 Cut out features, such as spikes, teeth, claws, eyebrows, and spots, from felt and a sheet of foam. Glue these onto the body, then stick on a pair of goggly eyes to bring your dinosaur to life!

Make a cuddly dinosaur instead by replacing the dried beans with toy stuffing.

TWISTY SOCK SNAKE

This twisty snake is cute, colorful, and super-easy to make.

1 Fill a sock with toy stuffing and insert a pipe cleaner through the middle, so it is contained inside.

2 Tie about six rubber bands at 2 inch intervals along the sock to create the round sections of the snake's body.

3 Sew a loose running stitch around the opening and pull the end of the thread until it closes together. Secure by tying a knot in the thread.

4 Cut out felt shapes to add to your snake, such as a pink forked tongue and diamond shapes to decorate its back. Sew or glue these into position.

eyes

diamond shapes

tongue

5 Finally, add some finishing touches to your snake. Sew on colorful beads for decoration and add goggly eyes to bring him to life.

A patterned sock will make your snake even more interesting.

PATCHWORK PICTURE

Pictures don't have to be painted. You can create a 3D picture using fabrics instead.

YOU WILL NEED:

- A 5 x 7 in. (12 x 17 cm) wooden frame, glass and backing removed
- String
- Staple gun and staples
- Scissors
- Paper
- Pins
- Assorted green, patterned fabrics
- Green and black felt
- Needle
- Embroidery thread
- Toy stuffing
- Long length of blue and purple yarn and ribbon
- Fabric glue
- 2 white and grey pom poms (see page 116)

1 Wrap string around your frame, leaving 1/2 inch (1.5 cm) spaces between the lengths. Staple the threads to the back of the frame and cut off the lengths at the front.

2 Cut out about five hill shapes from paper and use these as templates to cut out hills from the patterned fabrics and felt. Make sure the hills will fit in the lower half of your frame.

3 Sew the fabric hills onto a 5 x 7 inch (12 x 17 cm) rectangle of green felt, using a running stitch. Leave a space in each to insert a small amount of toy stuffing before sewing them closed. Trim the top of the backing felt into a curved hill shape.

4 To make the sky, weave the ribbon and wool through the lengths of string on the frame until half the frame is filled.

head

pom pom body

5 For the sheep, glue two pom poms to the hills. Cut out black felt heads and glue them into position. Finally, staple your hill landscape, facedown, to the back of your frame.

Why not try making a picture of the scene outside your window?

BURLAP POT WRAP

Work on your embroidery skills and brighten up a dull flower pot with this pretty wrap.

1 Gather the burlap fabric around the flower pot and tie it up at the top with a ribbon tied into a bow.

2 Using the fabric chalk, draw a tree design on one side of the burlap fabric. At the ends of the tree branches, draw circular shapes.

3 Begin your embroidery by using a back stitch to outline the tree trunk. Embroider the circles using colorful thread and a variety of stitches, such as chain stitch and satin stitch.

4 Sew on assorted beads and buttons to add a decorative finish.

Wrapped around a beautiful plant, this would make a wonderful Mother's Day gift.

BOUNCY BIRD

Hang this feathered friend next to your window in your room.

1 Wrap two rubber bands around a styrofoam ball so they cross over each other. Using yarn threaded onto an embroidery needle, thread the yarn over and around the rubber bands. (See page 80 for a similar method.)

2 Keep weaving until the ball is covered, changing yarn colors to make a striped effect. Tie a knot in your last thread and cut off the excess. You could leave some wool threads loose to attach beads for decoration.

98

3 Make a pair of wings by cutting out four identical wing shapes from felt. Sew the pairs together with a running stitch. Leave a space to insert a small amount of toy stuffing, then sew closed.

4 To make a tail, glue feathers onto the back of your bird. Glue the stiff quills under a section of woven wool. Glue or sew the wings onto the sides of the body.

5 Glue on on a folded diamond felt beak and add goggly eyes. Stitch a length of elastic thread to the ridge at the top so you can hang your bird.

Make your bird in colors that match your bedroom!

99

DOG PUPPET

This soft puppet is just as cute and cuddly as a real dog—but not as much work!

YOU WILL NEED:

- A sock
- Toy stuffing
- Pipe cleaner
- 3 rubber bands
- Needle
- Embroidery thread in assorted colors
- Large embroidery needle
- About 40 4 in. (10 cm) lengths of thick yarn
- Scissors
- Brown felt
- Goggly eyes
- Fabric glue
- Small bell
- Ribbon
- 2 wooden dowel rods

1 Fill a sock with toy stuffing and insert a pipe cleaner through the middle, so it is contained inside. Tie 3 rubber bands at regular spaces to create round body sections.

2 Sew a loose running stitch around the opening and pull the end of the thread until the opening gathers together. Tie a knot in the thread to secure.

3 Sew a running stitch all the way down the back of the sock body.

4 To make the dog's fur, thread each length of yarn through the running stitches along the back, using a large embroidery needle. Embroider a nose, mouth, and eyebrows onto the face. Stick on goggly eyes.

5 Cut out two felt ears and sew these onto the head. Sew the bell onto a length of ribbon and tie around the dog's neck. Finally, make a small hole in the underside of the head, and push one dowel rod into the hole. Repeat at the other end of the body.

Make a family of dogs using different colored socks and wool.

DRAWING MATERIALS

drawing pencil

wax crayons

Drawing Pencils

An HB pencil is recommended to begin with and then try B and 2B for softer shading. Don't try to shade with an H pencil as it is too hard. "H" pencils get harder as the numbers go up, and "B" pencils get softer as the numbers go up.

Colored Pencils

Colored pencils come in a huge variety of colors. Generally they are similar in hardness, but soft ones that can be smudged and blended are available too.

Watercolor Pencils

Watercolor pencils look similar to colored pencils, but they are soluble in water, which will give drawings a watercolor effect. You can dip them in water before drawing or color as normal and then brush water over the top.

Wax Crayons

Wax crayons are sticks of colored wax. They come in many colors and are great to use for rubbings as they are typically very blunt, which is good for shading large areas of color. They are also waterproof, so you can paint over the top and the wax color will show clearly through and will not run.

Inks

Drawing inks can be bought in small bottles. They can be diluted with water and applied with a brush or pen. Interesting effects can be created by dropping

inks

small blobs of ink onto wet paper and letting them flow. An ink pad is good for fingerprinting and can be made easily with a small piece of sponge lightly soaked with ink.

Pens and Markers

There are many different kinds of pens and markers available in different thicknesses and colors. Try experimenting with as many as possible to create lines, shading, textures and patterns.

For detailed work try fineliner pens in sizes 0.1 mm, 0.3 mm, 0.5 mm, and 0.7 mm. For thicker marks try markers with thicker tips.

Permanent markers are generally resistant to rubbing and water, but won't wash off most surfaces so you have to be very careful with them.

textured paper

Textured Paper

Paper can be bought in many different textures. Drawing on textured paper can give your drawings different effects, so it is worth experimenting with them.

glitter glue

Glitter Glue

Glitter glue can be bought in a bottle with a fine nozzle and is suitable for drawing fine lines.

permanent marker

fineliner

markers

colored pencils

PAINTING MATERIALS

Acrylic Paint

Acrylic paint comes in tubes. It is quite thick and a little can go a long way, so only use a small amount. You can thin it with water, but the colors are more vibrant if you use it without. When acrylic paint dries, you cannot erase it with water. It can only be painted over. It has a glue-like surface, once dry, that is waterproof.

paint palette

Paint Palette

A paint palette is a special surface used for mixing different colors of paint. Paint palettes can be place mats, a piece of acrylic glass, a paper plate, or cardboard covered in wax paper.

Cartridge Paper

Cartridge paper is an excellent choice for pencil and pen drawings. It comes in different thicknesses. The thicker versions will withstand being painted. Watercolor paper is specially designed for watercolor paints. It has a wonderful texture that is perfect for the delicacy of watercolor painting.

cartridge papers

Watercolor Paints

Watercolor paints can be bought as blocks with a palette or in small tubes. If you buy tubes, only squeeze a small amount onto a palette and mix with water. If using blocks, wet a paintbrush and stroke over the block and paint onto a palette. The more water you use, the lighter the color. If you want a very intense color, use only a little water—just enough to lift the color from the block.

acrylic paint

Paintbrushes

Paintbrushes come in many different shapes and sizes— round or flat, thick or thin. Use the right type of paintbrush for the kind of painting you are doing.

watercolor paints

paintbrushes

Small paintbrushes are ideal for adding detail and large, flat brushes are good for big, sweeping strokes. Clean brushes after you use them and they will last for a long time.

Materials to Add Texture

Texture can be added to paint using many different methods. Try mixing things like sand and glitter into your paint. You can add texture using white glue, letting it dry, and painting over the top. You can also paint with other tools besides paintbrushes, like sponges, cotton balls, and even your fingers!

Sponge

PRINTING MATERIALS

sponge brush

Poster Paint

Poster paints are good for projects that are printed on paper. But they do not mix well to make new colors.

Fabric Paint

Fabric paints are best for printing onto fabric, as they will not wash off or bleed into the material. They will need fixing with a hot iron before washing, but always make sure an adult does this for you. Make sure whatever you are painting onto has been washed first. Acrylic paint can also be used for printing on fabric, such as shoes or bags. It does not need to be heat set but will dry stiffer than fabric paint.

poster paint

Sponge Brush

A sponge brush is best when painting onto objects that are to be used to print with, because it will absorb excess paint. Use a sponge brush when the printing object is too large to fit onto a stamp pad.

Adhesive Foam Sheets

These are thick sheets of a lightweight but tough, bendy material, that are adhesive on one side. You can cut them into shapes and they bend without tearing.

fabric paint

adhesive foam sheet

colored paper

Colored Paper

Paper can be bought in many colors. Using colored paper can give your creations different effects, so it is worth experimenting with them. Almost any kind of paper can be used with these projects, as long as it can hold up to being painted.

Work Preparation

It's important to cover the work surface with plastic or paper to prevent any permanent accidents and to make cleanup easier. Inexpensive plastic tablecloths work well. Also, wearing an old shirt or an apron is a good idea to protect clothing. Be sure to have some baby wipes or paper towels handy to cleanup any spills or messy hands.

Printing Objects

Almost anything can be used to print with, as long as you ask permission first and it can hold up to being painted. Plastic toys and fruit and vegetables make great printing objects, as does anything with an interesting pattern or texture.

Floral Foam (oasis)

Floral foam is available from florists and garden centers. It is great to make a stamp from as it is very stiff and easy to carve designs into.

floral foam

OTHER MATERIALS

embroidery thread

yarn

Embroidery Thread

This is a type of yarn used especially for embroidery. It comes in loads of different colors.

Needles and Pins

Needles are pointed metal tools to sew with. They have a hole at the top called an 'eye' to thread yarn through. Pins are very similar to needles but don't have an eye at the top. They are used to hold fabric in place before sewing. Always ask an adult to help you with needles and pins. They can be very sharp.

pins

needle

Yarn

Yarn is like a very thick thread that comes in many different colors and thicknesses. It is usually used for knitting, but can be used for weaving and even embroidery.

Toy Stuffing

This is soft, white material, similar to cotton-balls. It is great for padding out your creations, to help them look more 3D. It also makes toys soft and cuddly!

toy stuffing

White glue

White glue is a widely-used, safe type of glue which is great for sticking paper and cardstock. It is sometimes called PVA (polyvinyl acetate) or school glue. White glue often comes in a squeeze bottle with a nozzle which makes it very clean and easy to use.

white glue

Dowel Rods

Dowel rods are solid, lightweight sticks used for adding support to your creations. They are usually made of wood or plastic. They are easy to cut to size, but always ask an adult to do this for you.

dowel rods

Fabric Chalk

Fabric, or tailors', chalk is a very hard type of chalk that is used to make marks on fabric. It is useful to draw out shapes that you need to cut out. The marks can be washed off.

fabric chalk

Foam Sheets

These are thick sheets of a lightweight but tough,

felt

bendy material. You can cut them into shapes, glue them, and bend them without them tearing.

foam sheet

Fabric glue

Fabric glue is the best glue to stick fabrics together, as it can be washed without coming unstuck.

Fabric

Fabric is any type of cloth. You can use old clothes to make your creations from, but always ask an adult before cutting anything up!

fabrics

Felt

This is a type of cloth that is usually soft and comes in loads of different colors. It is strong and will not fray when cut.

DRAWING TECHNIQUES

Tips on Cross-hatching

1. Keep your pencil well sharpened and try not to grip it too tightly. Begin with simple strokes all in the same direction, lifting the pencil up between each stroke.

2. Make long, light strokes with the side of the pencil point. Don't press too hard. If the strokes are too short they begin to look like furry caterpillars.

3. Make another layer of shading over the first in a different direction.

4. Repeat with a third layer in a different direction. Each different direction adds more tone to the shading, and makes it progressively darker and darker.

5. Velvety strokes can be used to finish off areas of shading. Glide the pencil back and forth very lightly over the darkest areas.

6. To make furry strokes, try holding the pencil a long way from its point. Hold it loosely and wiggle it across the paper.

Shading
Lines or other marks used to show gradual changes of color or darkness.

Texture
The appearance and feel of a surface.

Color Blending

You can use the cross hatching method to overlap and blend colored pencils together.

Colors which are close on the color circle wheel blend well together. For example, reds, oranges and yellows, blues, greens and yellows, or pinks, purples and blues.

Collage

A collage may include newspaper clippings, pieces of fabric, bits of colored or hand-made papers, portions of other artwork or words, photographs, and other objects. These can be glued onto paper or canvas in an arrangement of your choice.

Frottage

In frottage the artist takes a pencil or other drawing tool and makes a "rubbing" over a textured surface. The drawing can be left as it is or worked into.

Frottage can be made by laying sheets of paper over the surface and then rubbing over them with a soft pencil. It is best to keep the pencil lines in the same direction and to use the side of the point.

Perspective

Perspective rules help artists to draw in such a way as to make objects appear to be 3D. Remember that objects appear to be smaller when they are in the distance.

Experimenting

Trying things out to see what will happen.

PAINTING TECHNIQUES

Using watercolor

To apply color, use light colors first, then build up to darker colors. Let the paint dry before adding more, unless you want the colors to bleed and mix together.

If you paint a color onto paper, but decide you want it lighter, you can add water with a paintbrush to lift the paint off.

It is a good idea to use thick, heavy paper with watercolors, as you tend to use more water. Paper can only take so much water before it begins to break up.

Using Acrylic

To mix colors, always start with the lightest color on the palette. Add a little of the darker color at a time, until you are happy with the color you have mixed.

When painting, think about the direction of your strokes. Sometimes you can see the marks of brush hairs moving in a direction. Also think about the length of your strokes. Do you want long, sweeping strokes or quick, short flicks?

Adding Texture

To add a grainy texture, mix a small amount of sand or glitter with your paint before use.

To add a pattern, texture, or design with white glue, apply the white glue in the pattern or texture you want, allow it to dry completely and then paint over the top. White glue often comes in a squeeze bottle with a nozzle to make this easier.

To apply paint with a sponge, a cotton ball or fabric, dip the item into a small amount of paint and then dab it onto paper.

Wax Painting

When you paint on top of wax with a thin water-based paint, such as watercolor, an interesting effect happens. Because the paint cannot stick to the wax, you will be able to see the wax drawing through the paint. You can use a candle to draw with before applying the paint, but remember you won't be able to see what you are drawing! You can also use colored wax crayons to achieve this effect.

Transferring a Tracing

To transfer a tracing on tracing paper onto paper, turn the tracing paper onto its back and carefully draw over the lines in pencil. Next, flip the tracing paper back onto the right side and lay a sheet of paper underneath it. Carefully draw over the tracing with a heavy pressure on your pencil. The tracing should now have transferred onto the paper.

Sgraffito

With this technique you can scratch through paint to reveal a layer of color underneath. Apply blocks of bold color to thick paper with oil pastels, then apply a thick layer of black oil pastel over the top. Then, carefully scratch into the black with a sharp object.

PRINTING TECHNIQUES

Applying Paint

Paint is applied to the stamps and printing tools in different ways, depending on the tool or technique.

A sponge brush is used to apply paint to roller printing tools or to large printing plates. When the stamp is too big for a stamp pad, such as vegetable stamps or toys, a sponge brush is also used. Dip the sponge brush in paint and apply it to the item.

For small or delicate items, like floral foam stamps or modeling clay stamps, press them onto a homemade foam stamp pad to apply the paint. If paint is applied with a sponge brush, it will clog up the carved design lines.

The foam or sponge stamp is dipped into the paint until the bottom surface is covered. A fat paintbrush is used to apply paint for stenciling. Pour a small amount of paint into a plastic cup, dip the brush into the paint, then hold the stencil flat with one hand and tap the brush around the edges and open areas of the stencil. Do this until all of the open spaces of the stencil have been filled in.

Making a Stamp Pad

Some stamps, such as those made from modeling clay or floral foam, work best with a foam stamp pad that you can make yourself. Put a small sponge on top of a plastic lid. (If it's the type of sponge that is hard when dry, wet it first to soften it, then squeeze out all of the water.) Squeeze a small amount of paint onto the sponge, then use your fingers to spread it around. Use it just like a normal stamp pad, but add more paint as needed. Wash out the sponge when you are done.

Stenciling

Stenciling prints the negative spaces of a design. You can either make your own stencils out of paper, or use things like masking tape and stickers. Objects like bubble wands or plastic toys can also be used as stencils. Stencils are great to use when you want to repeat a design for a project.

Gluing

Glue can be used to create a rubbing plate or it can be used to attach thick yarn to cardboard to create a printing plate. For a rubbing plate, draw a picture onto a piece of cardboard, then trace over the picture with glue. Once dry, place paper on top of the rubbing plate and scribble over it with crayons to make the design appear. You can use as many colors as you want, overlapping them, or only use one color.

Toothbrush Spatter Paint

Spatter painting with a toothbrush looks like splattered spray paint but uses a toothbrush and paint. Squirt a small amount of paint on an old toothbrush, then with the bristles facing down, run your finger across the bristles toward you to spatter paint on the project. Use several colors for different colored spatters.

Monoprinting

Use this technique when you only want to make one print. It involves drawing directly into the paint on a paint palette. Spread a thin layer of paint onto a paint palette with a sponge brush, then draw a design into the paint with your finger, a paintbrush or the eraser end of a pencil. Remember that everything will print backwards, so if you want any writing, it needs to be backwards too. Place the printed side of the paint palette onto the project, pressing down on it to be sure the whole design prints, then carefully remove it.

OTHER TECHNIQUES

MAKE A POM POM

YOU WILL NEED:
- Scissors
- Cardstock
- Yarn

1 Cut two identical donut rings from cardstock and place them together.

2 Wrap the wool around the rings, going through the hole and around the outer edge. Keep wrapping until the hole in the middle is very tight.

3 Cut through the yarn around the edge of the ring, a layer at a time, until you meet the cardstock rings underneath.

4 Pass a length of yarn in between the two cardstock rings. Tie it tightly around all the yarn at the center. Now remove the cardstock rings and reveal your pom pom!

STITCHING WEAVING

Running stitch

Sew up and down through the fabric, making sure the stitches on both sides are kept the same size.

Blanket stitch

Push the needle through from back to front. At the front, level with your first stitch, push the needle through the fabric but come up again by going through the loop you have created with the thread.

Back stitch

Make a running stitch, then come up through the fabric a stitch ahead and stitch backwards to meet your first running stitch. Repeat in a neat line.

Weaving

Lengths of material are passed through a set of taut, spaced-out threads, in an alternate "over, under, over, under" pattern. This is repeated with many lengths so that they make an interlacing lattice. You can also weave "over and around" dowel rods in a cross shape (see woven mobile on page 80).

Chain stitch

Come up through the fabric and make a little loop, held in place with your thumb. Go back down through the fabric at the top and inside the loop. Come back up and forward a stitch length. Before pulling the needle all the way out, wrap the free thread under the needle and pull out to create your second loop.

Satin stitch

Mark out the shape you want and sew straight stitches closely together across the shape, taking care to keep the edges even.

117

INDEX

INDEX